The Healthy Indian

An Indian-Western Fusion Cookbook

Ravi Beech, MBA, Recipe Developer
Devika Sharma, BSc., Registered Dietitian (RD)

Foreword

This recipe book is a valuable resource for people looking to enjoy the flavours of Indian-Western cooking without the meals being high in sodium, saturated fat and sugar. With heart disease being the second leading cause of death in Canada (Public Health Agency of Canada, 2017) and the number one cause of death in the United States (American Heart Association Council on Epidemiology and Prevention Statistics Committee and Stroke Statistics Subcommittee, 2018), reducing the risk for this health issues is important. There are many factors like lifestyle (e.g. diet, exercise, healthy body weight, smoking, stress), demographics and other health issues that can affect the development of these conditions. While some risk factors cannot be controlled, making positive dietary changes may reduce the risk of developing heart disease (Public Health Agency of Canada, 2017). This book aims to deliver flavourful, low sodium, high fibre, protein packed and healthy fat meals and snacks – nutrients that are important to maintain good health.

Devika Sharma, RD

Table of Contents

6

Meet Your Flavours

Nine essential ingredients that need to be stocked in your kitchen

CARDAMOM (Elachi)
Flavour profile: pungent sweet flavour with a hint of spice
Appearance: small, brown seeds, found whole or ground
Proposed Health Benefits: antiseptic, enhance immune system

CLOVES (Laung)
Flavour profile: sweet and spicy
Appearance: dark brown in colour, available in pods (removed from the final dish) or ground
Proposed Health Benefits: antioxidant, antimicrobial

CORIANDER (Dhania)
Flavour profile: blend of lemon, sage and caraway
Appearance: fresh green leaves, whole dried seeds or ground form
Propose Health Benefits: anti-inflammatory, may aid in digestion

CUMIN (Jeera)
Flavour profile: warm and nutty
Appearance: small, black seeds
Proposed Health Benefits: aids in digestion, reduce allergy symptoms

GARAM MASALA
Flavour profile: rich, sweet and peppery
Appearance: blend of ground spices
Proposed Health Benefit: aids in digestion

GARLIC (Lahasun)
Flavour: sweet and spicy
Appearance: dried ginger, fresh ginger root
Proposed Healthy Benefits: cholesterol-lowering properties, anti-clotting, anti-inflammatory

GINGER (Adarak)
Flavour: sweet and spicy
Appearance: dried ginger, fresh ginger root
Proposed Healthy Benefits: antioxidant, anti-nausea, anti-inflammatory, antimicrobial

RED CHILI POWDER (Laal Mirch)
Flavour profile: spicy
Appearance: red powder
Proposed Health Benefits: anti-inflammatory

TURMERIC (Haldi)
Flavour prolife: earthy
Appearance: yellow-orange root or powder
Proposed Health Benefits: anti-inflammation

BAKED SAMOSA

Time: 60 minutes   Makes 20 servings.

1 tbsp avocado oil
1 onion, red, small chopped
1 tsp ginger, diced
1 tsp garlic, diced
1 tsp green chili, diced
1 c green peas
¼ c carrots, diced
½ tsp garam masala
½ tsp turmeric powder
1 tsp red chilli powder
½ tsp sea salt
4 large potatoes, boiled, peeled, cubed (approximately 5c diced)
½ c baby spinach, diced
½ Greek yogurt, plain, non-fat
½ tsp lemon juice
2 tbsp cilantro leaves
4 tbsp flax seeds
1 tbsp sesame seeds
20 spring roll wrappers, 8" each
1-2 tbsp avocado oil (for brushing as needed)

1. Preheat oven to 425F. Line large baking tray with parchment paper and set aside.

2. Heat oil in a large pan. Sauté onions until golden brown and then add ginger, garlic, and green chilis. Continue to sauté for 2 minutes.

3. Add peas and carrots and cook for 1 minute.

4. Add the garam masala, turmeric, chili powder and salt, and mix well for another 1 minute.

5. Add potatoes, spinach and Greek yogurt and cook for 1 minute. Remove from heat and add lemon juice, cilantro, flax and sesame seeds.

6. Fold spring roll wrapper into a samosa as outlined on page 33. Place on tray and repeat for the remaining potato mixture.

7. Brush samosas with oil and bake for 15 minutes. Reduce heat to 375F, flip samosas over and continue baking for an additional 10 minutes.

8. Once cooked, serve samosas immediately. For more flavour, pair with 1 serving of tamarind chutney (pg.30).

🌿 Dietitian's Note: This dish is a good source of healthy fats. The low sodium, high fibre and protein content make it a good substitute for the traditional samosa.

Nutritional Information (per one serving):
Energy: 130 kcal   Protein: 4g   Fat: 3.5g (saturated fat 1g) Carbohydrate: 23g
Fibre: 2g Sugar: 1g Sodium: 120mg. One serving is equivalent to 1.5 carbohydrate choices.

BAKED PAKORA

Time: 45 minutes
Makes 12 servings – 1 serving contains 2 pakoras.

Batter Mixture
2c chickpea flour
1 tsp red chili powder
½ tsp sea salt
½ tsp baking powder
1 green chilli pepper, diced
½ tsp chaat masala
½ c cilantro leaves
1 c Greek yogurt, plain, 2%
1 tbsp avocado oil
1c spinach, chopped
1 tbsp cumin seeds

Vegetable Mixture
1 onion, red, medium, chopped
1 yam, large, steamed, peeled and cubed
1 potato, large, steamed, peeled and cubed
½ cauliflower head, small, chopped into bite sized pieces (approximately 2 cups)

1. Preheat oven to 500F. Line large baking tray with parchment paper and set aside.

2. In a large bowl, mix the batter ingredients together to create a thick pancake like consistency. Add 2-3 tbsp of water if too dry.

3. Add the prepared vegetables to the batter mixture and mix well.

4. Hand press the vegetable mixture into 24 small patties and place on baking tray.

5. Bake for approximately 8-9minutes, flip the pakoras over, and continue to cook for another 8-10 minutes, or until golden brown.

6. Once baked, enjoy with a side of tamarind chutney (pg.30) and/or raita (pg.32).

🪶 **Dietitian's Note:** This dish is a good source of potassium and protein. Not only that, it is low in sodium and contains iron and calcium. Slash the salt – not the flavour!

Nutritional Information (per one serving):
Energy: 120 kcal   Protein: 6g   Fat: 3g (saturated fat 0.5g) Carbohydrate: 16g   Fibre: 3g Sugar: 4g Sodium: 135mg. One serving is equivalent to 1 carbohydrate choice.

CHAAT BOWL

Time: 45 minutes
Makes 8 servings.

Raita (see pg. 32)
Tamarind Chutney (see pg. 30)
Mango-Apple Slaw (see pg. 31)
Radish Slaw (see pg. 31)

15 oz chickpea, canned, low sodium, drained, rinsed
2 c mung beans, sprouted
1c chickpea, black gram, sprouted
1 yam, large, steamed, peeled, cubed in to 16 pieces
1 potato, large, steamed, peeled, cubed into 16 pieces
8 tbsp cilantro, chopped
8 tsp chaat masala
8 tbsp almonds, slivered

❯ *Recipe Tip: Make your own ginger and garlic paste by independently blending each ingredient with a small amount of water. Store in air-tight glass container for future use.*

1. Prepare the raita, tamarind, mango-apple slaw, and radish slaw. Set aside once done.

2. To assemble the bowls, place 1/4c chickpeas, 1/4c mung beans, 1/4c black gram, 2 pieces yams, and 2 pieces potato. Add 1 tbsp of cilantro and mix well.

3. Top each bowl with 2tbsp of raita, 1 tsp chaat masala, and 1 tbsp of tamarind, mango-apple slaw, radish slaw and almond slivers. Mix together and enjoy.

🪶 **Dietitian's Note:** This dish is a good source of protein, fibre, potassium, and calcium. Not only is this recipe full of flavour, it contains iron.

Nutritional Information (per one serving):
Energy: 350 kcal Protein: 16g Fat: 10g (saturated fat 1g) Carbohydrate: 46g Fibre: 12g Sugar: 11g Sodium: 260mg. One serving is equivalent to 2.5 carbohydrate choices.

3 medium yams, unpeeled
1 tbsp avocado oil
½ onion, white, medium, diced
1 tsp oregano seeds
1 tbsp cumin seeds
1 tbsp ginger puree
1 tsp green chili puree
¼ tsp black pepper, ground
4c chickpeas, drained
and rinsed
Cilantro for garnish

Dry Masala Mixture
1 tbsp garam masala
1 tsp cinnamon, ground
1 tsp nutmeg
1 tbsp chaat masala
1/8 tsp sea salt

Wet Masala Mixture
4c water
4 cardamoms
2 cloves
1 cinnamon stick
1 orange pekoe tea bag
1 tbsp tamarind
3 large tomatoes
4 tbsp non-fat Greek yogurt

YAM CHANNA MASALA

Time: 1 hour Makes 7 - 1 cup servings.

1. Steam yams. Once done, peel and mash into a puree.

2. Prepare wet mixture by bringing water to boil in a pot. Add cardamoms, cloves, cinnamon stick, tea bag and tamarind. Allow the contents to steep. Once complete, strain into a blender. Add tomatoes and yogurt and blend until wet masala mixture is of smooth consistency.

3. In a pressure cooker, heat oil over medium heat. Add onions and cook until golden brown. Add oregano, cumin, ginger puree, green chili puree, black pepper and 4 tablespoons of blended wet masala mixture. Mix and cook until golden brown. If too dry, add more wet masala mixture.
4. Add dry masala mixture and stir for 5 minutes.
5. Add chickpeas and gently mix for 5 minutes.
6. Add the remaining wet masala mixture, mix well and cover for approximately 30 minutes.
7. Add yam puree and mix thoroughly. Cook for an additional 20 minutes.
8. Once cooked, garnish with cilantro and serve.

Dietitian's Note: This dish is a good source of fibre, calcium, potassium and iron. If coconut oil or ghee were used this recipe would contain 2g of saturated fat.

Nutritional Information (per one serving):
Energy: 220 kcal Protein: 9g Fat: 4.5g (saturated fat 0.5g) Carbohydrate: 37g Fibre: 9g Sugar: 9g
Sodium: 260mg. One serving is equivalent to 2 carbohydrate choices.

Tempering

2 tbsp avocado oil
1 tsp cumin seeds
3 curry leaves, fresh or dried
1/8 tsp asafoetida
1 onion, white, large, finely chopped
1 tsp ginger paste
1 tsp garlic paste
2-3 green chillies, chopped
1 tomato, medium, pureed
2 potatoes, large, peeled, cut into ½ inch cubes
4 tbsp water
1 cauliflower head, medium, cut
¼ tsp sea salt
1 tbsp lemon juice, fresh
2 tbsp coriander leaves, finely chopped

Spice Blend

½ tsp turmeric powder
¾ tsp red chilli powder
½ tbsp coriander powder
½ tsp cumin powder
¼ tsp sea salt
½ tsp oregano seeds

ALOO GOBI

Time: 45 minutes   Makes 4 - 1 cup servings.

1. Heat oil in a large pan over medium heat. Once hot, add cumin seeds, curry leaves and asafoetida.

2. Once cumin seeds change colour and begin to crackle, add onions and cook until soft and translucent, about 5 minutes.

3. Add ginger and garlic paste, green chilies and tomato puree. Stir for 1 minute.

4. Add the spice blend and continue to stir for 1 minute.

5. Mix in the potatoes and continue to stir for 4 minutes. Add water to soften potatoes.

6. Add cauliflower and salt and stir for 3 minutes. Ensure all florets are well coated with spice blend.

7. Reduce heat to medium low, and cover for 10 minutes while stirring in between to prevent vegetables from sticking to pan. If vegetables are not cooked through, cover and continue to cook for 3-5 minutes.

8. Once cooked add lemon juice and garnish with coriander leaves.

Dietitian's Note: This dish is a good source of fibre, protein and potassium. It's also a source of calcium and iron.

Nutritional Information (per one serving):
Energy: 280 kcal   Protein: 8g   Fat: 8g (saturated fat 1g) Carbohydrate: 48g   Fibre: 9g   Sugar: 8g Sodium: 260mg. One serving is equivalent to 2.5 carbohydrate choices.

18

3c button mushrooms
3 tbsp Avocado oil 2
cinnamon sticks 1 bay
leaf, dried 2 cloves

1-star anise
1 tsp cumin seeds
1 tsp green chili, pureed
1 tsp garlic paste
1 tsp ginger paste
1 date, pitted, pureed
½ apple, medium, pureed
2 tbsp tomato paste
1 c Greek yogurt, plain,
non-fat
4 tbsp almond milk,
unsweetened
½ tsp fenugreek leaves, dried
1 c broccoli florets
1 medium orange bell
pepper, cut-up
¼ tsp of cardamom powder

Masala (pg. 32)
Marinade (pg. 32)

SHAHI BUTTON MUSHROOM

Time: 45 minutes + 4hours (for marinade)   Makes 4 - 1 cup servings.

1. Puree marinade ingredients together in a blender. Pour over button mushrooms and refrigerate for at least 4 hours.

2. In a wok, heat oil over medium heat. Add cinnamon sticks, bay leaf, cloves, and star anise. Allow ingredients to temper for 1 minute. Add cumin seeds and mix ingredients for approximately 5-6 minutes, or until the oil sputters.

3. Add green chili and stir for 30 seconds. Add garlic, ginger, date and apple puree and continue to stir for an additional minute.

4. Add tomato paste and stir for 2 minutes. Add the masala mixture and 1 tbsp water and stir for about 3 minutes to allow the flavours to blend together.

5. Add the marinated mushrooms and stir for 5 minutes, and then cover for 2 minutes.

6. Add the Greek yogurt and blend well. Add the almond milk and continuously stir for at least 6 minutes to allow the flavours to enhance.

7. Add the fenugreek leaves, broccoli and bell pepper. Mix for 3-5 minutes.

8. Cover the button mushroom curry and allow it to cook for 10 minutes. Once cooked, sprinkle cardamom powder and mix thoroughly. Garnish with cilantro (optional).

Dietitian's Note: This dish is a good source of calcium, potassium and iron.
To increase your fibre and protein intake, pair one serving of this dish with ½-1c of quinoa.

Nutritional Information (per one serving):
Energy: 220 kcal   Protein: 10g   Fat: 12g (saturated fat 1.5g)   Carbohydrate: 19g   Fibre: 4g   Sugar: 10g
Sodium: 210mg. One serving is equivalent to 1 carbohydrate choice.

Base
3c broccoli
1/2c mustard leaves, fresh
3 oz fenugreek leaves, fresh
1 green chili
4 mint leaves, fresh

2 tbsp avocado oil
1 tbsp ginger paste
1 tbsp garlic paste
½ red onion, medium, chopped
1 tsp cumin seeds
2 green cardamom pods
1/8 tsp asafoetida powder
½ tsp turmeric, powder
½ tsp red chilli powder
1/8 tsp sea salt
3 tomatoes, medium, diced
½ tsp fennel powder
1 tsp coriander powder
½ tsp garam masala
2 cloves
1 tbsp lemon juice
15oz canned chickpeas, low sodium, rinsed and drained
1 tbsp corn flour

CHANNA SAAG

Time: 45 minutes
Makes 4 - 1 cup servings.

1. Prepare base mixture by steaming broccoli, mustard leaves and fenugreek leaves. Drain excess water and add to food processor. Add green chili and mint leaves, and pulse until thick consistency.

2. Heat oil in medium pot over medium heat. Once hot, add ginger paste, garlic paste, onions, cumin seeds, cardamom, asafoetida, turmeric, chili powder and salt. Cook until onions are soft and translucent, about 5-7 minutes.

3. Add tomatoes, fennel powder, coriander powder, garam masala, cloves, and lemon juice and continue to cook for another 5-6 minutes.

4. Stir in the chickpeas. Once blended, add corn flour and ½ of the base mixture and mix well. Cook for 5-6 minutes.

5. Add the remaining base mixture, mix well, cover and reduce heat to low-medium. Cook for 15 minutes.

Dietitian's Note: This dish is a good source of calcium, iron, potassium and fibre. Make sure you rinse the canned chickpeas well to remove excess sodium.

Nutritional Information (per one serving):
Energy: 260 kcal   Protein: 11g   Fat: 9g (saturated fat 1g) Carbohydrate: 36g Fibre: 9g
Sugar: 7g   Sodium: 170mg. One serving is equivalent to 2 carbohydrate choices.

¼ tsp avocado oil
½ tsp fenugreek seeds
½ tsp curry leaves, dried
or 2 fresh leaves
1 onion, red, medium and sliced
½ tsp sea salt
½ tsp turmeric
1 tsp garam masala
1 tsp ginger, minced
1 tsp garlic, minced
½ tsp red chilli pepper (reserve ¼ tsp for later)
½ c chickpea flour, ground
4c Greek yogurt, plain, 2% (reserve 1 c for later)
4 potatoes, medium, parboiled, skinless, cut-up
1L water
¼ tsp ginger, minced
1 tbsp oregano leaves, dried
¼ tsp coriander, ground
¼ tsp onion powder
¼ tsp garlic powder
1 tsp poppy seeds
1 tsp sesame seeds
1/4c cilantro, chopped (optional)
1 tbsp lemon juice (optional)

YELLOW POTATO CURRY

Time: 1 hour   Makes 8 - 3/4 cup servings.

1. Heat oil in pan over medium heat. Once ready, add fenugreek seeds and curry leaves and cook for one minute.

2. Add onions, salt, turmeric and garam masala. Once onions are translucent, add ginger, garlic, and ¼ tsp chilli pepper. If paste too dry, add 1 tbsp of water at a time to achieve a smooth consistency. Roast for approximately 2 minutes.

3. While spice paste is roasting, blend chickpea flour and 3c of Greek yogurt in a large bowl until smooth consistency achieved. If mixture is too thick, add 1 tbsp water to thin it out.

4. Pour yogurt mixture over the spice mixture and mix well.

5. Mash potatoes into the curry mixture and mix well.

6. Add water, ginger, remaining red chili, oregano, coriander, onion and garlic powder to the mixture and mix well. Cook for approximately 20-25 minutes over medium heat while stirring every 5 minutes.

7. Add the remaining Greek yogurt, blend well and cook for an additional 15 minutes while stirring every 5 minutes.

8. Once cooked, mix in poppy and sesame seeds. To increase sourness, add lemon juice. Garnish with cilantro and serve with brown rice.

🌿 **Dietitian's Note:** This dish is a good source of calcium, potassium, and protein.

Nutritional Information (per one serving):
Energy: 210 kcal Protein: 15g Fat: 5g (saturated fat 2g) Carbohydrate: 27g Fibre: 3g
Sugar: 7g Sodium: 180mg. One serving is equivalent to 1.5 carbohydrate choices.

RICE PUDDING

Time: 50 minutes
Makes 6 – 1/2 cup servings.

1/4c brown rice, medium grain, dry,
soaked overnight
8 sprigs saffron
1 cinnamon stick
5c 1% milk
4 dates, pitted, pureed
1 apple, medium, pureed
5 green cardamoms
1 tsp vanilla bean powder (optional
for flavour)
¼ tsp vanilla extract
2 eggs, large
18 almonds, blanched and shredded

1. Boil rice, saffron, cinnamon stick and milk in a deep pot until rice is cooked and milk thickens, approximately 30 minutes. Stir occasionally to prevent sticking.

2. Add dates and apple puree, cardamoms, vanilla extract and powder. Reduce heat to simmer and cook for 10 minutes.

3. In a separate bowl, whisk the eggs until smooth. Add 1c of the rice mixture to the whisked eggs and mix well. Add egg-rice mixture to the pot and mix well until custard-like consistency achieved.

4. Remove from heat and top with almonds, mix and serve either warm or chilled.

🍃 **Dietitian's Note:** This dessert is a good source of calcium and protein. Not only that, it is low in sodium.

Nutritional Information (per one serving using eggs):
Energy: 200 kcal   Protein: 11g   Fat: 6g (saturated fat 2g) Carbohydrate: 26g   Fibre: 2g
Sugar: 16g   Sodium: 135mg. One serving is equivalent to 1.5 carbohydrate choices.

PROTEIN PINNI

Time: 45 minutes
Makes 25 servings.

3/4c peanut butter, all natural, reduced fat, creamy
1.5 tbsp gram flour
½ tbsp coconut flour
2 tsp ginger, ground
½ tsp green cardamom, powder
10 dates, pitted
1c hazelnuts
1/3 c water (to be added 1 tbsp at a time as needed)
1 tbsp chia seeds
1/4c almonds, sliced

1. Line baking tray with parchment paper and set aside.

2. Heat peanut butter in a pan over medium heat. Add gram flour and coconut flour and sauté for 5 minutes.

3. Add ginger, cardamom powder, dates and hazelnuts and continue to sauté for 1 minute. If mixture is too dry, add 1 tbsp of water at a time to achieve a doughy texture. Remove from heat and set aside. Let mixture sit for approximately 5 minutes.

4. Add chia seeds and mix well.

5. Using a small spoon scoop out the mixture, form a ball and place on baking sheet. Repeat with the remaining mixture and top each ball with 1 almond sliver.

6. Place tray in fridge and let it cool for approximately 30 minutes.

7. Store in air-tight container and refrigerate.

🌿 Dietitian's Note: These are a good source of healthy fats and contains protein. Both nutrients help with feeling full. These are also low in sodium and contain potassium.

Nutritional Information (per one serving):
Energy: 100 kcal Protein: 3g Fat: 8g (saturated fat 1g) Carbohydrate: 5g Fibre: 2g Sugar: 3g Sodium: 40mg. One serving is less than 0.5 a carbohydrate choice.

TURMERIC TEA

Time: 10 minutes
Makes 4 - 1cup servings.

1/2c water
1 orange pekoe or earl grey tea bag
2 cloves
1 cinnamon stick
4 cardamoms
1/8 tsp all spice
¼ tsp ginger, chopped
9 saffron threads
1 tbsp fennel seeds
1/2 tsp turmeric powder
4 dates, pureed
4c milk, 1%

1. In a medium pot, boil water and then add tea bag, cloves, cinnamon, cardamom, all spice, ginger, saffron threads, fennel seeds, turmeric and dates. Continue boiling for approximately 5 minutes.

2. Add milk and continue to boil until a rolling boil occurs. Mix well and remove from heat.

3. Strain mixture, top with cinnamon and serve immediately.

Dietitian's Note: This tea is a good source of vitamin D, calcium and protein. Not only that, it is low in sodium and contains no added sugars.

Nutritional Information (per one serving):
Energy: 140 kcal   Protein: 10g   Fat: 3g (saturated fat 1.5g) Carbohydrate: 22g Fibre: 3g
Sugar: 17g   Sodium: 135mg. One serving is equivalent to 1.5 carbohydrate choice.

MANGO MINT CHUTNEY

Makes 35 -1tbsp servings

1 mango, large
1c mint leaves
¼ c cilantro leaves
1 onion, red, chopped
3 green chillies
½ lemon, juiced
1 garlic clove
½ tsp sea salt

1. Blend all of the ingredients together into a smooth paste.
2. Store tightly in glass jar and keep refrigerated.

TAMARIND CHUTNEY

Makes 35 – 1 tbsp servings

2 tbsp avocado oil
1 red chilli, whole, dried
1 green chilli, diced
1 tsp cumin seeds
1 cinnamon stick
1 tsp mustard seeds
3 curry leaves
2c water, boiled
1c tamarind
3 dates, pitted, diced
1 tomato, red, large diced

1. In a large pan, heat oil over medium heat. Add red chilli, green chili, cumin seeds, cinnamon stick, mustard seeds, and curry leaves. Allow flavours to develop and cumin to darken, approximately 3 minutes.
2. Add water, tamarind, dates, and tomatoes to the pan and boil until thick consistency achieved, approximately 15 minutes.
3. Once desire consistency achieved, allow chutney to cool, store in a tightly sealed glass jar and refrigerate.

RADISH SLAW

Makes 8 -1tbsp servings

2 tbsp lemon juice
1 radish, red, large, shredded
1/16 tsp sea salt
¼ tsp turmeric, powder

1. Mix all of the ingredients together in a large bowl.
2. Store in air-tight container and keep refrigerated.

APPLE-MANGO SLAW

Makes 8-1tbsp servings

¼ apple, granny smith, large, shredded
1/8 tsp cumin powder
1/8c flax seeds
½ tsp garlic, minced
2 tbsp lime, juice
¼ mango, large
¼ pomegranate
1/8 tsp sea salt
1/8c sesame seeds
¼ c sunflower seeds, hulled

1. Mix all of the ingredients together in a large bowl.
2. Store in air-tight container and keep refrigerated.

1c Greek yogurt, plain, non-fat
½ tsp sea salt
½ tsp black pepper
½ tsp garam masala
1 tbsp water
1 tbsp cilantro leaves, fresh

RAITA

Makes 16-1tbsp servings

1. Mix all the ingredients together and serve fresh.

MASALA

(for Shai Button Mushroom recipe)
1 tsp turmeric powder
1 tsp cumin seed powder
1 tsp coriander powder
½ tsp red chili powder
1 tbsp water

MARINADE

(for Shai Button Mushroom recipe)
¼ c pineapple (fresh or frozen)
1 tbsp cilantro
1 tsp garlic puree
1 tbsp chaat masala
1/8 tsp sea salt
1 tbsp water

HOW TO FOLD A SAMOSA

1. Fold 1 square pastry sheet in half. If you are using a rectangular shaped pastry sheet, you may need to trim it.

2. Take the top right corner of the folded pastry sheet and fold past the centre to form a triangle. The right corner should now line up with the bottom of the pastry sheet. There should now be extra pastry hanging over the bottom right edge.

3. Fold the left corner over the already formed triangle to form another triangle. There should be extra pastry hanging over the bottom left edge. Pick up the folded pastry to form a cone.

4. Holding the cone-shaped pastry in one hand, fill with 2 tbsp of the samosa mixture.

5. Once samosa is filled, fold over the top remaining pastry to seal it closed. You may need to pinch the corners of the samosa to ensure proper sealing.

MEET THE AUTHORS

Ravi Beech completed her B.A. (major psychology) from Simon Fraser University graduating as the valedictorian of her class, and then went on to complete her MBA from Duke University. During the course of her undergrad, Ravi internationally competed, and won multiple titles, as a Giddha dancer. She performed for the opening and closing Vancouver 2010 Olympic ceremonies, was a National BC Finalist for Miss Universe Canada, and is a professional actress/model. Ravi is a recreational cook and recipe developer with a main focus on creating vegan, vegetarian and gluten free meals. She is the founder of raviliving.com sharing healthy lifestyle tips for busy professionals. Born and raised with Ayurvedic healthy living principles, she brings over 20 years of authentic traditional Indian cooking. Through this book she hopes readers will discover a healthier and flavourful way to prepare meals at home.

Social Media Handles: Instagram: @raviliving   Facebook: @raviliving   Twitter: @raviliving

MEET THE AUTHORS

Devika Sharma, a registered dietitian, received her first BSc (major Biology) from Simon Fraser University and earned her second BSc (major Dietetics) from the University of British Columbia. She currently holds a position as a renal dietitian in an outpatient hemodialysis unit. Although renal disease is her area of expertise, she has a great deal of interest and experience providing nutritional consulting to clients with other conditions such as cardiovascular disease, GI disease, diabetes and obesity. She is the founder of One More Bite (a Vancouver based nutrition consulting company) that aims to provide accurate dietary information to assist with prevention, intervention and treatment of nutrition impacted diseases. In addition to her dietetic career, she is a part time research assistant employed with the University of British Columbia in which she has collaborated on various manuscripts. When it comes to food and nutrition, Devika believes in balance. Her goal is to provide evidence-based nutrition therapy to help with disease prevention, intervention and treatment, while educating readers how to maintain flavour in their favourite foods.

Social Media Handles: Instagram: @onemorebite.dietitian   Facebook: @onemorebite.dietitian   Twitter: @one_more_bite_

Credits:
Food Photography: Devika Sharma   Instagram: @onemorebite.dietitian
Headshots: Yvonne Yiru Xu   Instagram: @walkingonadream.5

References
American Heart Association Council on Epidemiology and Prevention Statistics Committee and Stroke Statistics Subcommittee. (2018). *Heart diseae and stroke statistics 2018 update: a report from the American Heart Association.* Retrieved from Professional Heart Daily: https://healthmetrics.heart.org/wp-content/uploads/2018/02/At-A-Glance-Heart-Disease-and-Stroke-Statistics-2018.pdf

Public Health Agency of Canada. (2017, February 10). *Heart Disease in Canada.* Retrieved from Government of Canada: https://www.canada.ca/en/public-health/services/publications/diseases-conditions/heart-disease-canada.html

97766763R00022

Made in the USA
San Bernardino, CA
26 November 2018